Time Under Tension

Time Under Tension

Tactical Training

Josh Bryant and Adam benShea

Time Under Tension: Tactical Training

JoshStrength, LLC and Adam benShea

Copyright © 2020

Table of Contents

Time Under Tension: Tactical Training

Introduction

Sometimes, words fail us. At other times, a word captures an elusive instinct.

The word *synchronicity* is defined as "the simultaneous occurrence of events which appear significantly related but have no discernable causal connection."

As a concept, the famed psychologist Carl Jung suggested that events are "meaningful coincidences" if they occur with no causal relationship yet seem to be meaningfully related.

Many of us spend much of our lives going through our days like a pack animal wearing blinders, dutifully following the predetermined path to our next turn at the animal trough. A bleak thought? Perhaps, but perhaps because it rings true.

However, every now and then, we look up, we look aside, or maybe we look inside and we discover rare moments of grace, beauty, and indescribable meaning. Things connect and make sense in an unusual way. To miss such moments is to do an incredible disservice to the universe.

It was one such moment of an indefinable but undoubtedly important connection which led to our introduction to the idea of time under tension.

Freshman year is an indoctrination time for the high school athlete. This initial period serves to set the tone for a high school career, which for some will be that short span they will spend a lifetime revisiting over beers, hot wings, and discussions about their glory days. For others, the time spent in high or secondary school sports will be a formative experience in an athletic ascension which stretches into the broad territory of adulthood. In either case, your freshman year is the beginning of an impactful journey.

Well before our freshman year, we had gotten a jump start on our physical culture campaign by training with weights, entering the boxing ring, and familiarizing ourselves with various martial arts. Nonetheless, our freshman football coach was a rousing character who would serve to inspire our spirit and open our eyes to new ideas.

On the field, he showed the value of a clearly followed plan. In conversation, he displayed a romantic affection for the love of life. And in the weight room, he demonstrated the value in sustained intensity and tension for developing muscles.

A veteran of the Vietnam conflict, Coach Walker would speak candidly: "Look, tigers, you're gonna have some rough times in life. Times of tension. What you do during those times will not only define your character, but it could also mean whether you live or die.

"When you find yourself in a bit of a bind, in the midst of a rough go, don't stop! Don't wallow! Keep moving. Keep moving forward."

This idea was illustrated one day in the school weight room. Of course, we already had some experience with the iron. But Coach Walker had a different kind of workout in mind.

"Okay, tigers, here's the plan. We're going to do a circuit workout. You're going to pick a weight and stay with it for 30 seconds. Make it a heavy weight. Be audacious. Be bold with the weight you pick. Go heavy, and, no matter what, keep moving the weight. If you're only doing partial reps, that's fine. Keep moving the weight. Keep going. Keep moving forward."

The weight room was far from state of the art. Most of the options were Universal machines. So we moved through our stations at machine chest press, the triceps pressdown, the lat machine, and other similar movements.

No matter what, we kept the weight moving.

At the end of the workout, we felt like we had an epiphany, or a moment of truth and clarity usually associated with religion. Our pump was unreal, and we felt a rush of virility surging through our bodies.

This was our first introduction to time under tension training.

Ed Brown, courtesy of James Allen

Time Under Tension (TUT) Defined

In general, time under tension may be defined as the period spent performing muscular contractions during a strength training movement. Most often, the timing monitors the length of performed reps and sets.

We can unpack this general definition. When lighter weights are utilized, the so-called time under tension may also include a period when high-threshold motor units are not firing. Light weights do not offer the required load for muscle growth, even if the muscles are under a degree of relative tension for a prolonged period of time. Or, for instance, repetitive endurance movements like running or swimming require a level of effort that is low and well below the maximal amount that could potentially be produced.

So, the application of time under tension training for muscle growth is performing the maximum number of reps in the specified time, with maximum force, load, and intensity. This means that you want to keep the weight heavy and moving. The experience of time under tension should be working at a consistent tempo. Not too fast, not too slow, but a consistent tempo.

Scientists have hypothesized for some time that muscle hypertrophy is not purely a function of rep ranges, but the actual duration of the set.

For example, one recent study from McMaster University in Canada published in the *Journal of Physiology* concluded that prolonged muscle contraction was the most important variable for increasing muscle size. The study compared light loads using a tempo of one second up and one second down or using slow reps of six seconds up and six seconds down. The study asserted that the slow reps were superior because of the prolonged time the muscle was under tension.

Turning to "lab coats" for serious muscle-building advice should be done with a grain of salt. Science needs to be the guiding light for training, but not the only source of guidance.

Studies on training can have flaws. Most notably, most studies are typically performed on malnourished, sleep-deprived, hard-partying college kids, not the old heads who have been slinging serious pig iron in the trenches for years.

The aforementioned study compared explosive repetitions and slow repetitions with 30 percent of the subject's one-rep max. No one serious about getting stronger or packing on as much muscle as possible is doing 30 percent of their one-rep max for serious work sets. To put it in perspective, that would mean if you bench-press 200 pounds, you would work out with 60 pounds. Now, if your goal is packing on serious muscle, you're going to want some more poundage.

Guidelines for TUT

A couple of days after we had our first taste of time under tension training, the initial pump had subsided but the excitement had not. At that time, keeping us away from the gym was like keeping a sailor on board a ship during shore leave; it wasn't going to happen.

We soon found ourselves at our gym getting ready for the next workout. Now, in those days and at that gym, we liked to scan the territory to see which of the local characters were in attendance. Bouncers from the local peeler bar, veterans turned tactical athletes, mystical strength gurus, and ex-jocks were the general classifications of the various types who made up our community in this haven of strength.

This motley crew, all of whom were united in their pursuit of strength, could be thought of as our community, but they also made a tribe of mentors. Sure, they passed on insights about training. But they also offered advice well beyond the weight room.

Bouncers would warn us of the pitfalls of romancing strippers.

Ex-jocks would explain the benefits and detriments of living with your parents well into middle age as a means to save money for supplements and have more time to train.

Strength gurus would explain the therapeutic value of tantric meditation.

So, with potential wisdom spouting up across the chrome terrain, we wanted to know who was in the gym.

Our initial survey was cut short by a guttural grunt from over near the dumbbell tower. Old as dirt and tougher than a cheap steak, there was Bosco. Decked out in overalls and a longshoreman beanie, he looked every bit the part of a pumped-up retired dockworker, probably because that is what he was.

Finishing up the last reps of his workout, Bosco called us over.

"Hey ya fellas! Come over and say hey to ole Bosco."

Now, Bosco always talked in the third person—not because he was pompous or pretentious, but just because he liked the sound of his name. He told us once that it was a nickname taken from a chocolate syrup that he liked as a kid. Actually, we never knew his real name.

"Hey Bosco, what's going on?"

"Oh, not too much. Just finishing up this curl workout with some barbells," he said while breaking into a smile that revealed he had lost more teeth than he had left.

Although the bare torso beneath his overalls was broad and developed, his body had the imprint of a hard life. Old, faded dark blue tattoos, sun spots, and scars covered his muscular frame. The beanie perched on the top of his head did little to hide his complete baldness.

"What kind of workout?" we asked. We were always looking for new strength ideas.

"You see, boys, it's a workout where you kind of just keep going. You pick up some heavy weight with both hands, and you just keep lifting."

This was ringing some bells with what we had just heard from Coach Walker a couple of days ago.

"Could you tell us more?" Our interest was most certainly piqued.

"Well, boys, I'm going to get a little philosophical here." He paused to see whether we objected to that. When our silence implied consent to go on, he continued.

"Here it is. I had a rough go. I grew up in the Dust Bowl during the depression, and my family made the trip out west to escape all that. And like a lot of Okies, we ended up in Bakersfield. My dad took a job on the oil fields and I picked fruit. When World War II started, I was too young to enter the service, but I was able to get on a merchant marine ship. After the war, I stayed down by the sea, working the docks. First over in the Red Hook section of Brooklyn, you know, with all those racketeers controlling everything. Later, I worked in the rough-and-tumble Oakland docks.

"Where am I going with this? you may be wondering. I tell ya where. Life is rough, sometimes. And, you see, what I learned is this: You got to keep going. Even if it's partial steps forward, you got to take those steps."

At this point, the bells of synchronicity were ringing in our heads. This was the same message Coach Walker had just shared! During rough times, you got to keep moving forward. Keep going!

Now we weren't mystics or spiritual pilgrims, but it sure felt like the universe was telling us something.

Apparently, Bosco could tell he had our attention. So he kept going.

"Now this life philosophy, if you want to call it that, is what I bring to my training. What I'm trying to say is that I make workouts like a metaphor, that's a word my old lady taught me. She taught school.

"I find a heavy weight and I take it in my hands."

While he said that, we watched his calloused, meaty paws wrap around the iron bar of a barbell. As his fist clinched around the long, thin cylinder, vascularity lit up his thick forearms like Fourth of July fireworks in the night sky.

"Okay," Bosco spoke through gritted teeth, or what was left of them. "I'm going for 15 reps here. But I might only hit 10 good, clean ones."

We watched as the weight exploded up, but then he slowly lowered the weight back down. He did this again and again, just barely getting 10 reps. It was clear that he hit muscle failure. Yet, he didn't stop. He grinded out five more partial reps.

Placing the barbell down, Bosco took a long exhale. Then he spoke to us over his shoulder.

"Fellas, I could have stopped around eight or nine. Things were tough there. Instead, I kept going. I got my 15 reps. Those last reps weren't ideal. It wasn't pretty. But I reached my goal and that...that is always beautiful."

With that, Bosco's face broke out into a full gummy grin.

As for us, we stood there basking in this synchronous moment. The simultaneous occurrence of a life lesson and an innovative workout was something we knew we would remember. And now we are sharing with you.

About the Time Under Tension: Tactical Training Program

Coach Kelly Weaver, a Texas boxing icon, says, "You are a bull in that ring. You dictate where the fight moves and remain in control. If there is one thing I taught you, kid, it's ring generalship."

Let's take this concept of ring generalship and apply it to training. We will call it pig iron generalship. Get in the weight room and control the pig iron at a pace where you are completely in control of the weight and dictating the physiological magic that is about to emerge.

Your intention is the "general," and the weight pile is the army that follows your orders!

Make sure you set the right tempo for the weight. Don't go buck wild explosive with weights. Similarly, don't go in slow motion. On isolation exercises, your intention needs to be on maximal contraction of the targeted muscle and feeling it work. On compound movements, focus on great technique, moving the weight from point A to point B. When it's time, explode as hard as possible in a compensatory acceleration style (which we will specify below).

If done with the right mental intention and physical direction, the execution of an exercise should metamorphose into a profound experience. This intention needs to be radically different from any exercise experience you have had during this finite existence.

If you want to see a demonstration of the appropriate cadence in action, watch our "Time Under Tension" series on the Jailhouse Strong YouTube channel.

This training is very fatiguing. But let's remember the wisdom of psychologist William James from more than 100 years ago:

"If an unusual necessity forces us onward, a surprising thing occurs. The fatigue gets worse up to a certain point, when, gradually or suddenly, it passes away and we are fresher than before! We have evidently tapped a new level of energy. There may be layer after layer of this experience, a third and fourth 'wind.' **We find amounts of ease and power that we never dreamed ourselves to own, sources of strength habitually not taxed, because habitually we never push through the obstruction of fatigue.**"

The key to this program is not just the controlled pace, but what happens after you can no longer complete full reps.

When you hit failure with a weight, KEEP GOING!

Continue the set with partial repetitions, and once you hit failure with partial repetitions, continue without dropping the weight and squeeze the targeted muscles as hard as possible isometrically. Flex those bad boys with everything you have! Mental intention and physical direction will be everything in this workout.

Program Pillars

Start by picking a weight you can use for 8 to 12 reps.
Perform 30-second sets for week 1, and you will increase duration each week.
When you hit failure, continue the set with partial repetitions. Once you hit failure with partial repetitions, continue without dropping the weight and squeeze the targeted muscles as hard as possible isometrically.
Rest for 90 seconds between sets.
Do three total sets.

Program Progression

We cannot emphasize enough that no matter what happens, do not stop until you reach the specified time. Yes, this is why this program is only four weeks; it is very extreme. EVERY PROGRAM IS FOUR WEEKS AND FOLLOWS THE SAME PROGRESSION.

After the first week, keep the weight the same but increase the duration of each set by five seconds. Over the four-week progression, the sets should look like this:

Week #	Set Duration
Week 1	30 seconds
Week 2	35 seconds
Week 3	40 seconds
Week 4	45 seconds

If you do well with this right off the bat, a second option is to keep the duration of time the same but increase the weight used each week by 5 to 10 percent. Below is an example of how this would work.

Week #	Set Duration	Weight Used
Week 1	30 seconds	**80 lbs.**
Week 2	30 seconds	**85 lbs.**
Week 3	30 seconds	**90 lbs.**
Week 4	30 seconds	**95 lbs.**

Because of the extreme fatigue from this type of training, you're generally going to reduce the weight by 25 percent each subsequent set (however, if a set was achieved and you recover well, by all means, keep the weight the same).

For example, if you start a set with 100 pounds, set two would be with 75 pounds and set three with 55 pounds. This is a recommendation, not a rule; the rule is what weight to start with for set one.

IF YOU CAN USE THE SAME WEIGHT FOR EACH SET, YOU SHOULD!

Never forget the key to this program: KEEP THE WEIGHT MOVING.

And when the weight won't move, SQUEEZE!

Remember the Following Points:

- **Unless specified (with strongman events and specific core lifts), when you reach muscular failure, perform partial reps. Once you fail on partial reps,** squeeze the weight as hard as you can until you hit the prescribed time.

- Any percentages are based on YOUR CURRENT maxes; we recommend starting at 95 percent of your current, true one-repetition maximum (a 400-pound squat would count as 380).
- Strongman exercises can be swapped with their "kind." For example, a carrying exercise should be swapped with a carrying exercise.
- Speak to your physician before engaging in this program.
- If you have high blood pressure, heart issues, and/or poor conditioning, avoid this program.
- For compound squats and deadlifts, execute them in a movement intention/compensatory acceleration training (CAT) style as explosively as possible, moving the exercise from point A to point B with perfect technique.
- Execute isolation exercises by focusing specifically on the muscle you are targeting and feeling, not just moving, the weight.
- Focus on great technique with strongman events. We would prefer you work slightly slower with perfect technique (this is not a contest, and doing so decreases the likelihood of injury).
- Exercise substitutions are listed below.
- All substitutions should be for the same intensity, TUT, or rep scheme, with the equivalent rest break.

- Do not increase weight on squats and deadlifts. If they are easy, explode harder. Do not exceed reps.

- For strongman events that must be completed in specific time under tension periods, IF FORM BREAKS DOWN ON, STOP, rest, and then complete the next set with reduced weight.

Ed Brown, courtesy of James Allen

Gas Station Ready—Tactical Hypertrophy

The term *tactical athlete* is quickly becoming a buzzword in the world of strength and conditioning. A relatively new term in the realm of sports and military training, a tactical athlete is an individual with the requisite ability, strength, and stamina to successfully function on the battlefield. For instance, first responders are professionals who require physical preparation for occupational performance.

Tactical athletes deserve respect because they are some of the greatest athletes on Earth.

Tactical athletes personify the "Gas Station Ready" mentality because they don't have the luxury of not being ready. If they are not ready, the result is failed missions, lost battles, and casualties.

Operating with those kinds of stakes requires a kind of hypervigilance which some would call paranoia. You stay ready so you don't have to get ready.

A tactical athlete requires specific tactical vocational skills alongside the necessary physical ability, strength, and conditioning levels. Examples are a structural firefighter rescuing an obese person from a burning building or an infantry soldier on a long-range mission with over 100 pounds of external gear.

Tactical athletes need to be mobile, agile, strong, and explosive, yet they also have to have the base conditioning to repetitively exhibit these qualities under life-threatening fatigue and duress.

Tactical athletes need a solid strength base without sacrificing conditioning.

High levels of strength, a high percentage of muscle mass, and a low percentage of body fat are effective predictors of how well a tactical athlete will perform under the load of their specific vocational requirements. This means that a broad back, jacked arms, and a lean waist don't just look good in that form-fitting tailored suit you picked up for the banquet following the alumni game of your old high school.

So, yes, muscle hypertrophy goes far beyond being Chippendales ready for the male revue stage (although that will be a by-product, but with a slightly truculent twist). Muscle growth makes the tactical athlete more effective in the field. Additionally, a muscled-up look is one of the best ways to deter someone looking to take your ride, your life, or your lady.

Civilians

Staying Gas Station Ready with tactical training just makes sense. It is the type of protocol that will prepare you for your amateur boxing match at the local veterans' building, your regional obstacle course race, or your tryout for the master's rugby league. You will also cultivate a level of physical and mental preparedness that will take you from merely surviving to a place of thriving.

Now, welcome to the Gas Station Ready movement. We are honored to have you on board. Remember this: YOU ARE THE MOVEMENT!

Proudly hashtag #GASSTATIONREADY

To benefit the most from this type of programming, an athlete should be able to meet the following requirements, at a minimum:

> **2.0 x bodyweight squat**
> **2.2 x bodyweight deadlift**
> **1.2 x bodyweight pull-up**
> **1.2 x bodyweight bench press**
> **0.8 x bodyweight overhead press**

The stronger you are, the more you will benefit from the Gas Station Ready TUT Tactical Hypertrophy program. If limit strength is an issue, we recommend following the Pig Iron program found in our book *Jailhouse Strong* or the limit strength program from our book *Grapple Strong*.

The objective is to be mobile, agile, and hostile, but durable enough to endure a dustup in an East LA swap meet or confidently walk into a dive bar in Hong Kong as the only foreign national, with the poise to not just have a few cocktails but maybe even throw your hat in the karaoke ring.

Gas Station Ready Time Under Tension Program

Day 1

Exercise	Weight or Intensity	Sets	Reps	Rest Interval	Special Notes
Plyometric Push-Ups	BW	3	3	45 sec	Focus on pushing up as high as possible.
Incline Dumbbell Bench Press	8 – to 12-rep max	TUT	3	90 sec	
Towel Pull-Ups	8 – to 12-rep max	TUT	3	90 sec	
Band-Resisted Feet-Elevated Push-Ups	8 – to 12-rep max	TUT	3	90 sec	

Continue

Exercise	Weight or Intensity	Sets	Reps	Rest Interval	Special Notes
Seal Dumbbell Rows	8 – to 12-rep max	TUT	3	90 sec	Any rowing substitution must be chest-supported or seated.
Standing Cable Flys	8 – to 12-rep max	TUT	3	90 sec	Feel over weight, squeeze contraction one second.
Band-Resisted Neck Rotations	Light	2 each way	20	60 sec	Your hand can be used for manual resistance if no band is available.

- **Plyometric push-ups can be replaced with medicine ball chest passes or Smith machine bench press barbell throws with 20 percent of your 1RM.**
- **Incline dumbbell bench presses can be replaced with decline or flat dumbbell presses, or any incline, decline, or flat chest press machine variation.**
- **Towel pull-ups can be replaced with assisted towel pull-ups, or towel lat pulldowns, with a machine or against bands.**

- **Band-Resisted Feet-Elevated Push-Ups** can be replaced with any loaded push-up variation or dumbbell bench press variation.
- **Seal dumbbell rows** can be replaced with any machine row or chest-supported row. **DO NOT do bent-over rows or freestanding rows**—the objective is to build the upper back and save the lower back.
- **Standing cable flys** can be replaced with band flys, dumbbell pause floor flys, or any chest fly machine.
- **On band-resisted neck rotations, the band can be replaced with cable.**

Day 2

Exercise	Weight or Intensity	Sets	Reps	Rest Interval	Special Notes
Box Jumps	BW	1	10	30 sec	Focus on jumping as high as possible.
Squats	75%	2	6	120 sec	Do in a compensatory acceleration style.
Backward Sled Drags	A weight you could go 100 feet with an all-out effort	3	TUT	90 sec	

Continue

Exercise	Weight or Intensity	Sets	Reps	Rest Interval	Special Notes
Bulgarian Dumbbell Split Squats	12 – to 15-rep max	2	TUT	45 sec	2 sets each leg. Hold dumbbell in one hand, one hand on rack.
Nordic Leg Curls	Maximum	3	3	45 sec	5-second eccentric
Machine Biceps Curls	8 – to 12-rep max	3	TUT	90 sec	Any machine
Hammer Curls	15 – to 20-rep max	3	TUT	45 sec	Both arms together
Neck Extensions	30 – to 40-rep max	3	20	45 sec	

- Box jumps can be replaced with broad jumps. Jump to 75% of a maximum jump, focusing on jumping as high as possible; DO NOT RISK IT with excessive height. Besides risking safety, excessive height encourages a focus on landing in extreme hip flexion, the converse of an explosive jump, which is the objective.
- Squats can be replaced with any squatting variation. You can add 5 to 15 pounds weekly; focus on moving the barbell as fast as possible with perfect technique.
- Backward sled drags can be replaced with walking lunges or leg presses.
- On Bulgarian dumbbell split squats, if your left leg is grounded (the working side), grasp the squat

rack with your left hand and place the dumbbell in your right hand. Your left hand can be used to help maintain balance and guide you through sticking points. If there is an imbalance between sides, do TUT on your weaker side, then match reps on your stronger side.

- Nordic leg curls can be replaced with three sets of six reps with maximum intensity of leg curls or glute ham raises. Band assisted is okay, and, if applicable, a weighted vest or any other form of resistance can be used.
- Machine biceps curls can be replaced with inverted bodyweight curls, barbell curls, or EZ curl biceps curls.
- Hammer curls can be replaced with machine rope hammer curls, fat bar curls, or reverse curls.
- Neck extensions can be done with a plate behind the head, a band, cables, or a harness.

Day 3 (Optional, but Highly Recommended)

Exercise	Weight or Intensity	Sets	Reps	Rest Interval	Special Notes
Jump Rope	BW	4 sets	TUT	30 sec	
Tempo Run	BW	15 min	See description.	See description.	See description.
Pro Agility Run	BW	6	1	30 sec	75% of max speed
L Drill	BW	6	2	30 sec	75% of max speed

- For jump rope, do not exceed the TUT guidelines; focus on fast feet! Quick feet and agility are the objective.
- For tempo runs, athletes need to run the following distances based on bodyweight: < 200 pounds, run 110 yards; 201 to 250 pounds, run 85 yards; 251 to 299 pounds, run 65 yards; 300+ pounds, run 50 yards. Runs should be at 70% of maximum speed; focus on stride and technique, and walk back to the start. Start the next tempo run when your heart rate is in the 115 to 130 beats per minute range. Speed, sets, and distance will not progress as your conditioning improves; you will get in more runs.
- The pro agility run is to keep you agile. Stay at 75% of your max speed; remember, day 2 you went all out—DO NOT EXCEED 75%.
- The L drill is also to keep you agile. Stay at 75% of your max speed; remember, day 2 you went all out—DO NOT EXCEED 75%.

Day 4

Exercise	Weight or Intensity	Sets	Reps	Rest Interval	Special Notes
Seated Dumbbell Press	8 – to 12-rep max	3	TUT	90 sec	
Dumbbell Rear Delt Partial Flys	Same weight as seated dumbbell press	3	TUT	90 sec	6-inch ROM facedown on incline— "pulses"

Lateral Raises	15 – to 20-rep max	3	TUT	90 sec	Standing
Smith Machine Close-Grip Bench Press	10 – to 15-rep max	3	TUT	90 sec	
Overhead Rope Triceps Extensions	10 – to 15-rep max	3	TUT	90 sec	
Triceps Ladder	BW	??	100 reps	N/A	Keep track of time to completion.
Side Necks	30 – to 40-rep max	2	20	45 sec	Each way
Neck Flexions	30 – to 40-rep max	2	20	45 sec	Each way

- Seated dumbbell presses can be replaced with Viking presses or any standing or machine press variation.
- Dumbbell rear delt partial flys can be replaced with any reverse pec deck or rear delt dumbbell fly.
- Lateral raises can be done with dumbbells or a machine; any lateral raise seated or standing variation is permissible.
- Smith machine close-grip bench presses can be replaced with close-grip push-ups or dips.
- Overhead rope triceps extensions can be replaced with overhead dumbbell extensions or band overhead extensions.

- On the triceps ladder, keep track of time; reps do not increase weekly. The objective every week is to beat your time from the previous week.
- Side necks can be done with a plate behind the head, a band, cables, or a harness.
- Neck flexions can be done with a plate behind the head, a band, cables, or a harness.

Day 5

Exercise	Weight or Intensity	Sets	Reps	Rest Interval	Special Notes
Backward Overhead Med Ball Throws	5 to 10 pounds	1	12	30 sec	
Deadlifts	65%	1	10	30 sec	Do in a compensatory acceleration style.
Farmer's Walk	A weight you could go 150 feet with an all-out effort	3	TUT	90 sec	Straps are okay; wear if needed.
Snatch-Grip Shrugs	25 – to 30-rep max	3	TUT	90 sec	
Arm over Arm Sled Pulls	A weight you could go 60 feet with an all-out effort	3	TUT	90 sec	

One-Leg Romanian Deadlifts	8 – to 12-rep max	2	5	As needed	One dumbbell each hand
Landmine Anti-Rotationals	Heavy as possible totally strict	3	4	45 sec	4 each way

- Backward overhead med ball throws can be done with a medicine ball or plate; standing broad jumps can be substituted.

- For deadlifts, either trap bar or straight bar is okay; weight, sets, reps, and rest interval will not change, so intention is on great technique with maximum speed.

- For the farmer's walk, walk at a steady pace; implements, dumbbells, a trap bar, or spud straps are okay. The farmer's walk can be replaced with any weighted carry event.

- Snatch-grip shrugs can be replaced with dumbbell shrugs or Hise shrugs.

- Arm over arm sled pulls can be replaced with T-bar rows or seated rows.

- One-leg RDLs can be replaced with split-stance RDLs with a barbell or dumbbells.

- Landmine anti-rotationals can be replaced with the palloff press with bands or a cable.

Day 6 (Optional, but Highly Recommended)
Repeat Day 3

Day 7 REST DAY

Ed Brown, courtesy of James Allen

Chippendales Ready Time Under Tension Program

So, you've been working as a barback at some upscale sake lounge. Now, who should walk in but your current Instagram crush. Without skipping a beat and not noticing you, she ambles past you, with her rolling hips, only to cop a feel of the bartender's beefed-up biceps.

She sits, sips sake, reads a magazine, and occasionally looks up to visually undress the beloved bartender.

Man, you're tired of playing second fiddle to that bartender.

After getting her fill of the bartender, your crush heads off into a warm afternoon. But she left behind her magazine. It's a slow day. You don't have much to do. So, why not flip through the pages? Past the tips on fellatio and recipes for the perfect cosmo, right there in the middle of the magazine, you stop and do a double take.

There it is! Your destiny awaits! A group of tanned, half-naked, muscled-up cowboys with grins the size of Texas and obvious stage generalship are commanding an adoring crowd of screaming ladies.

It's obvious; these dudes are having the time of their lives.

These guys are Chippendale dancers.

Right then and there, you decide to quit being a stiff and join the team. You are going to become Chippendales ready! #Chippendalesready

So, whether you want to get ready for the bodybuilding stage, prep for the Chippendales stage, up your Tinder game, or just strut your stuff at the high school reunion in front of the newly divorced head cheerleader who missed her chance with you 15 years ago, this is the plan for you.

Day 1

Exercise	Weight or Intensity	Sets	Reps	Rest Interval	Special Notes
Incline Dumbbell Bench Press	8 – to 12-rep max	TUT	3	90 sec	
Neutral-Grip Pull-Ups	8 – to 12-rep max	TUT	3	90 sec	
Dips	8 – to 12-rep max	TUT	3	90 seconds	Lean forward to emphasize chest.
Seal Dumbbell Rows	8 – to 12-rep max	TUT	3	90 sec	Any rowing substitution must be chest supported or seated.
Standing Cable Flys	8 – to 12-rep max	TUT	3	90 sec	Feel over weight, squeeze contraction one second.
Push-Ups—Incline Dumbbell Flys—Flat Dumbbell Bench Press	See guideline below	Max	12—12—20	None	Complete as many rounds as possible in 8 minutes.

- For the push-ups to incline dumbbell flys to flat dumbbell bench press, do 12 reps of push-ups and incline flys and 20 reps of the dumbbell bench press. Use half of a maximum weight for these rep ranges. Move from exercise to exercise as fast as possible; complete as many circuits as possible in eight minutes.

Day 2

Exercise	Weight or Intensity	Sets	Reps	Rest Interval	Special Notes
Machine Squats	8 – to 12-rep max	3	TUT	90 sec	
Chin-Ups	8 – to 12-rep max	3	TUT	90 sec	Hands supinated
Lying Leg Curls	8 – to 12-rep max	3	TUT	90 sec	
Leg Extensions	15 – to 20-rep max	3	TUT	90 sec	
Romanian Deadlifts	8-rep max	3	TUT	90 sec	Add 5 to 10 pounds a week.
Bulgarian Squats—Leg Extensions—Sissy Squats	See guideline below	3	12—20—12	None	Complete as many rounds as possible in 8 minutes.

- **For the Bulgarian squats and sissy squats, use your bodyweight. For the leg extensions, use a weight you can do 40 reps with for one all-out set. Move from exercise to exercise as fast as possible; complete as many circuits as possible in eight minutes.**

  Romanian Deadlifts are done in the fashion of a 5 second negative. Perform a five second negative, but keep positive explosiveness. Cables, barbells or Dumbbells are permissible. DO NOT REACH FAILURE on this exercise. If form deteriorates, STOP!

Day 3

Exercise	Weight or Intensity	Sets	Reps	Rest Interval	Special Notes
Seated Dumbbell Press	8 – to 12-rep max	3	TUT	90 sec	
Dumbbell Rear Delt Partial Flys	Same weight as seated dumbbell press	3	TUT	90 sec	6-inch ROM face-down on incline— "pulses"
Lateral Raises	15 – to 20-rep max	3	TUT	90 seconds	Seated
Smith Machine Close-Grip Bench Press	10 – to 15-rep max	3	TUT	90 sec	

Overhead Rope Triceps Extensions	10 – to 15-rep max	3	TUT	90 sec	
Triceps Ladder	BW	??	100 reps	N/A	Keep track of time to completion.
Crucifix Dumbbell Holds	Heavy as Possible	3	30-sec hold	90 sec	

- Complete Triceps Ladder with as few sets as possible

Day 4
Off

Day 5
Repeat Day 1

Day 6
Repeat Day 2

Day 7
Repeat Day 3

Day 8
Off

Day 9 start Week/Cycle 2, do this for four weeks/ cycles.
If you use this program, remember to hashtag
#chippendalesready

Ed Brown, courtesy of James Allen

Quarantine Ready Time Under Tension Program

After spending three years in a monastery, you decide to walk away from your life as a monk. A six-month vow of silence made you realize that this monastic order was more concerned with maintaining institutional continuity than the spiritual quest for enlightenment.

As you walk away, you realize you never really fit into society anyway.

You pitch a tent and set up base away from society, where you wake up at 6 a.m. every morning, eat granola, and enjoy the company of your only friend—a bear named Three Toes.

Life is good. You found what you are looking for.

But something is still missing!

You think back to your childhood days at the YMCA and their motto of a sound mind, body, and spirit. The mind and spirit are there, the body is not.

Going into town to a gym is out of the question. So you decide to embark on a bodyweight training journey.

An isolated existence can be a product of many circumstances. You could be quarantined by choice, by government order, or because you're doing a stint in the slammer after going overboard with corporal punishment on the teenager who stole your kindergartner's bike. Whatever the specifics of your case, this is the plan for you.

Days 1 & 4

Exercise	Weight or Intensity	Sets	Reps	Rest Interval	Special Notes
Pull-Ups	BW	3	TUT	90 sec	
Dips	BW	3	TUT	90 sec	
Inverted Rows	BW	3	TUT	90 sec	

Continue

Exercise	Weight or Intensity	Sets	Reps	Rest Interval	Special Notes
Decline Diamond Push-Ups	BW	3	TUT	90 sec	
Head Nods	Head	3	TUT	90 sec	
Triceps Ladder	BW	??	100 reps	N/A	Keep track of time to completion.

- Complete Triceps Ladder with as few sets as possible

Day 3 OFF

Days 2 & 5

Exercise	Weight or Intensity	Sets	Reps	Rest Interval	Special Notes
Leg Raises	BW	3	TUT	90 sec	
Jackknife Sit-Ups	BW	3	TUT	90 sec	
Lunges	BW	3	TUT	90 sec	Alternate legs
Prison Squats	BW	3	TUT	90 sec	
Vertical Jumps	BW	3	TUT	90 sec	
Nordic Leg Curls	BW	3	3	As needed	5-second negative

Day 4

Exercise	Weight or Intensity	Sets	Reps	Rest Interval	Special Notes
Burpees	BW	10	TUT	60 sec	If this is easier, go faster!

Day 7 OFF

If you use this program, remember to hashtag #quarantineready

Final Thoughts

Whether you want to be built to impress at the Dean Martin cover band and martini night at the Ritz or just want to be able to tear up an unruly patron at a Calcutta dive bar, this program will get you there.

These battle-tested programs have been proven over and over in the trenches. Make them work for you.

If you have the will, we have the way.

Made in the USA
Columbia, SC
04 July 2021

41391165R00029